KATHERINE AND HUGH COLLEDGE

FAST FORWARD

21 PIECES FOR VIOLA PLAYERS

BOOSEY & HAWKES

Following on from *Stepping Stones* and *Waggon Wheels* this collection of twenty-one pieces explores 0–12–3–4 and 0–1–2–34 finger patterns. New rhythms and compound time are introduced, along with a wider range of expression marks and some varied bowings.

Some of the piano introductions are optional. In such cases, the introductory 'rest' bars have not been included in the viola part, but the length of the introduction is indicated at the top of each piece. Bar numbers in the pieces with optional introductions begin in the first bar of the violin part.

KATHERINE & HUGH COLLEDGE
London, UK

Kathy and Hugh met in East London where they both worked as peripatetic teachers at Newham Academy of Music. Hugh had previously studied oboe and piano at Trinity College London while Kathy was a violin student at NE Essex Technical College (now Colchester Institute). They were both born in London but Kathy started to play the violin in New Zealand where she lived in her youth.

Their association with Boosey and Hawkes began in the 1980s when the couple added to the pieces Kathy had written for her pupils in Newham to create *Stepping Stones* and *Waggon Wheels*. They later added *Fast Forward* and *Shooting Stars*, as well as a number of works for beginner string ensemble in the *Simply 4 Strings* series. More recently they contributed two new string quartets to the *4 Strings* series edited by Liz Partridge.

They moved to Norfolk in 1995 and continued to teach in the State and Independent sectors until their retirement.

Published by Boosey & Hawkes Music Publishers Ltd
Aldwych House
71–91 Aldwych
London
WC2B 4HN

www.boosey.com

ISMN 979-0-060-13426-5 | ISBN 978-1-78454-362-4 (viola part & CD)
ISMN 979-0-060-13543-9 | ISBN 978-1-78454-467-6 (viola part & piano accompaniment)

Printed by Halstan:
Halstan UK, 2–10 Plantation Road, Amersham, Bucks, HP6 6HJ. United Kingdom
Halstan DE, Weißliliengasse 4, 55116 Mainz. Germany

Piano performance and audio production by Robin Bigwood
Viola performance by Jane Norman

Music origination by Moira Roach

Cover illustrations by Jo Moore
Cover design by Chloë Alexander Design

The composers would like to thank Liz Hilling for suggesting the title *Fast Forward*.

The original edition of this book was dedicated to the pupils and staff at Newham Academy of Music.

FAST FORWARD

21 PIECES FOR VIOLA PLAYERS

PERFORMANCE & ACCOMPANIMENT TRACKS

Demonstration and piano accompaniment backing tracks are available for all pieces in this book.

Visit www.boosey.com/colledge to access digital audio files.

01 Track 01 is a tuning note. Ensure you are in tune with this before using the rest of the audio tracks.

02 **Demonstration tracks** are included for all pieces. Track numbers are shown in black circles.

03 **Backing tracks** are included for all pieces. Track numbers are shown in grey circles.

1. Winter's night

02 03

Optional intro: count 2 bars

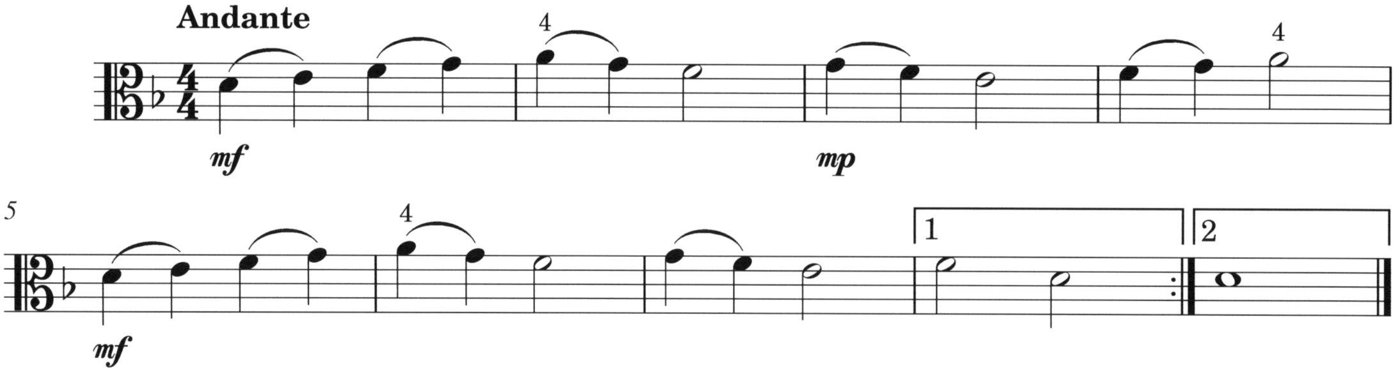

2. Lazybones

04 05

Optional intro: count 2 bars

3. Hallowe'en

06 07

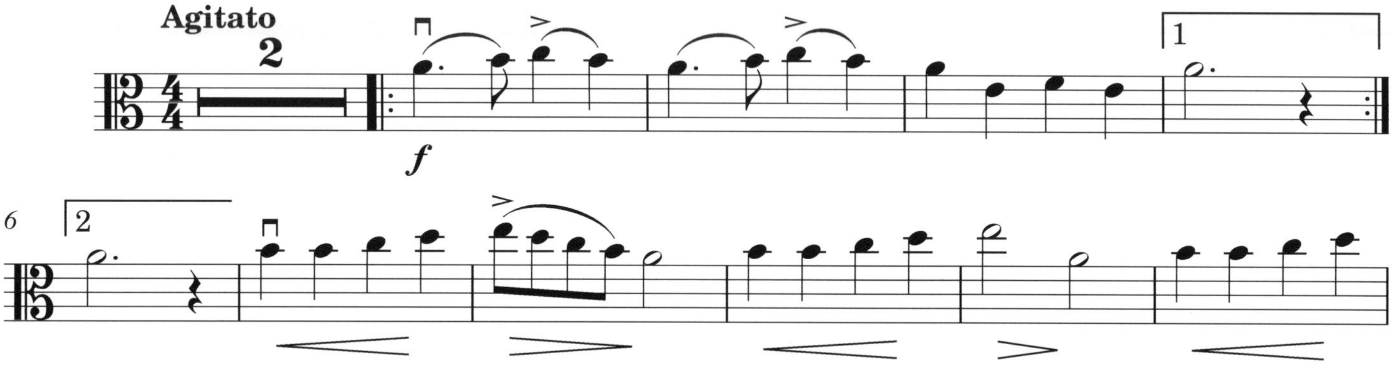

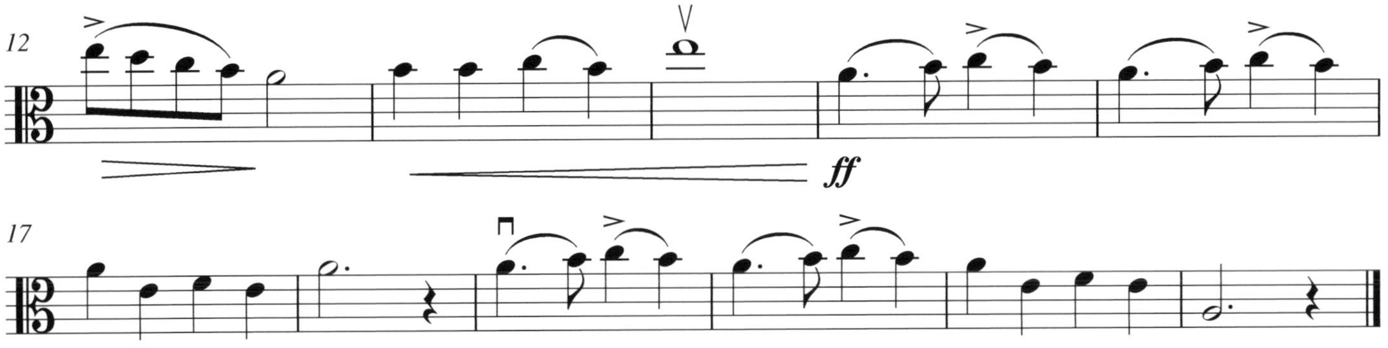

4. Singapore sunset

08 09

Optional intro: count 4 bars

Brightly, but not too fast

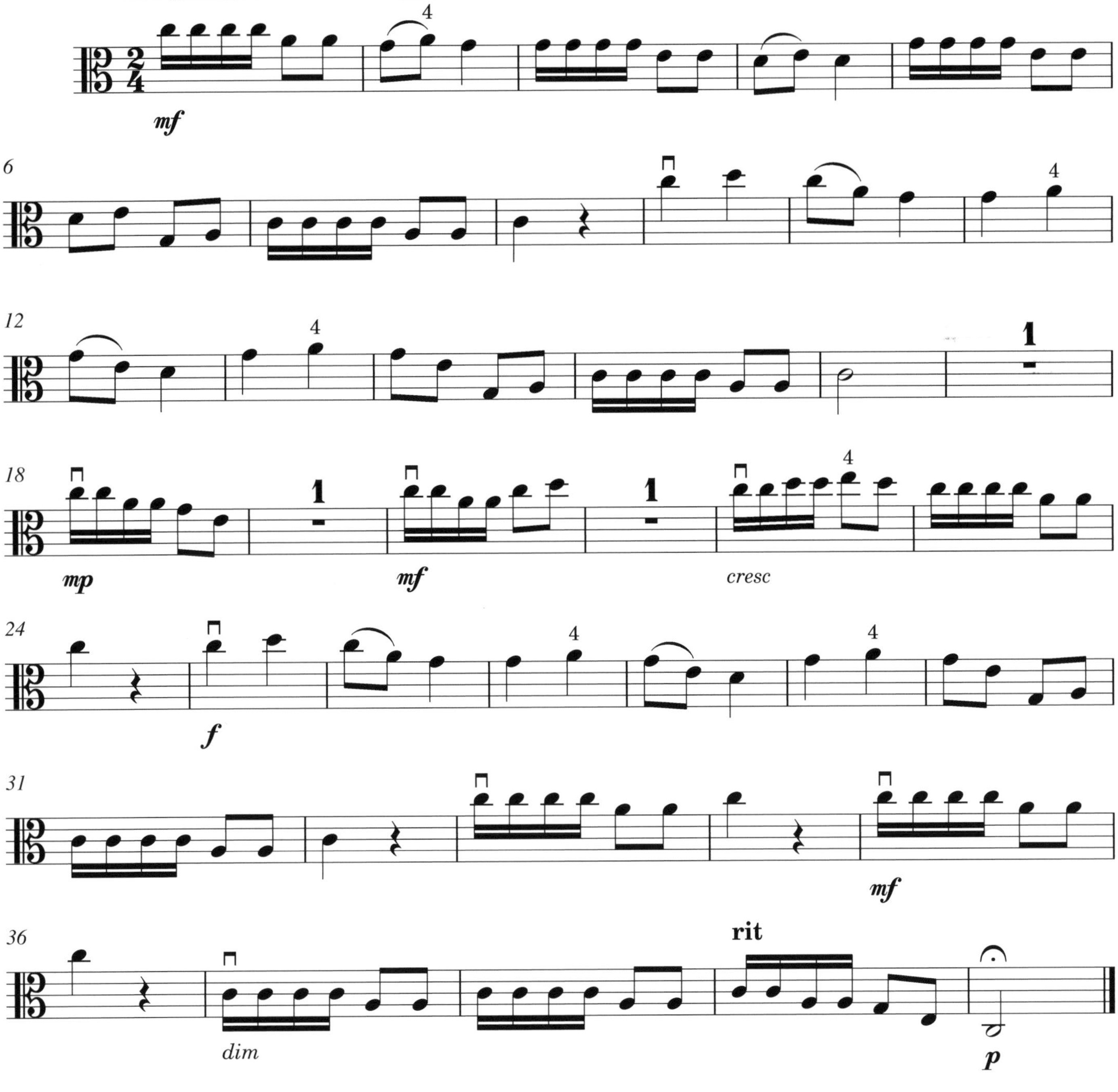

5. Polly's polka

10 11

6. Windmills

12 13

Optional intro: count 4 bars

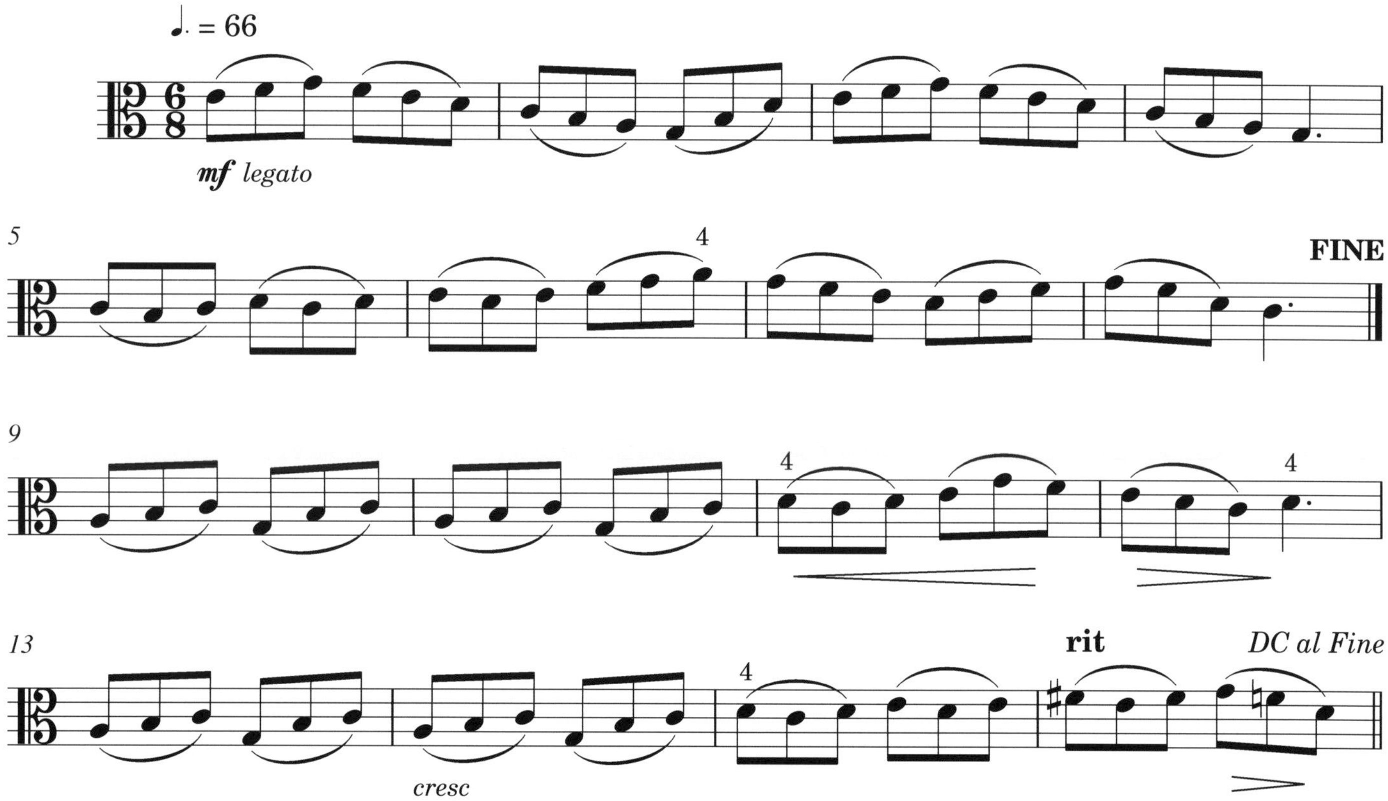

7. Boogie-woogie

14 15

8. At harvest time

16 17

9. Clever clogs! (a clog dance)

18 19

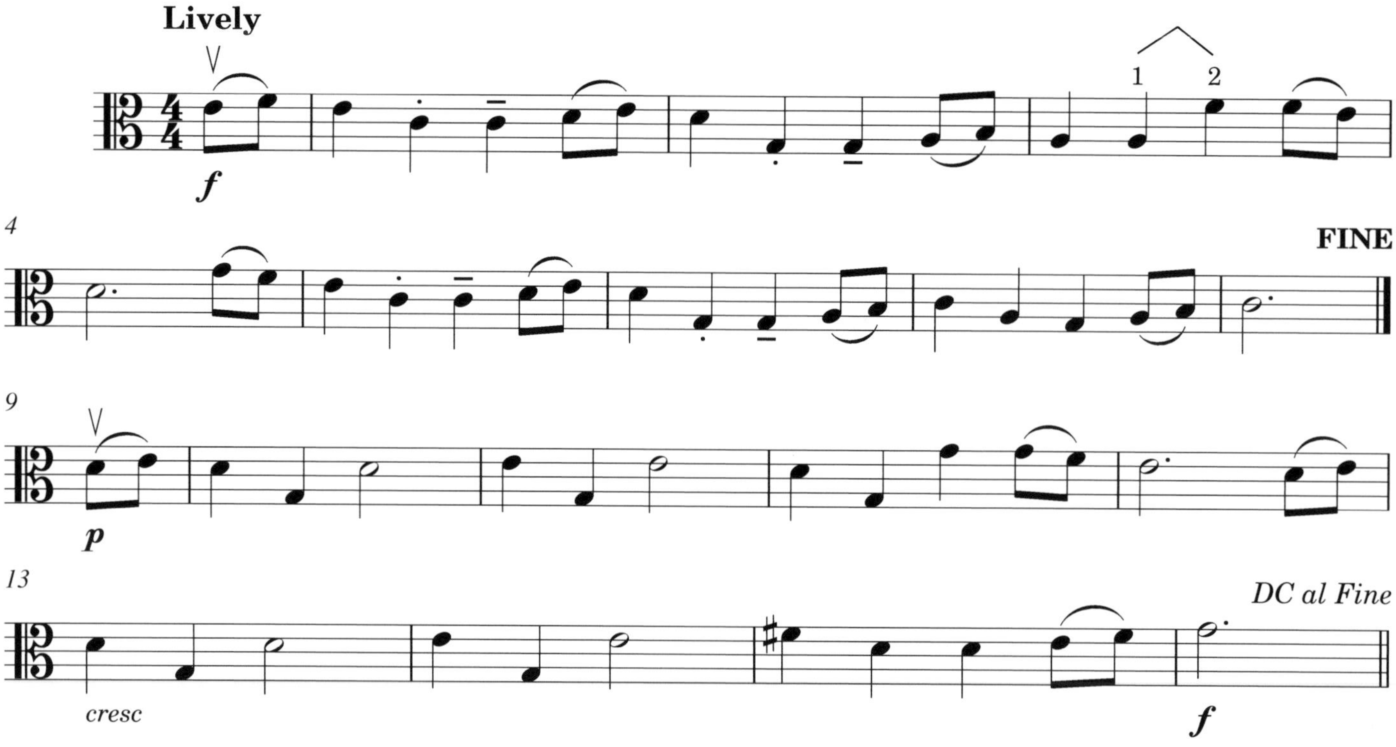

10. Weeping willow

20 21

11. Drifting

22 23

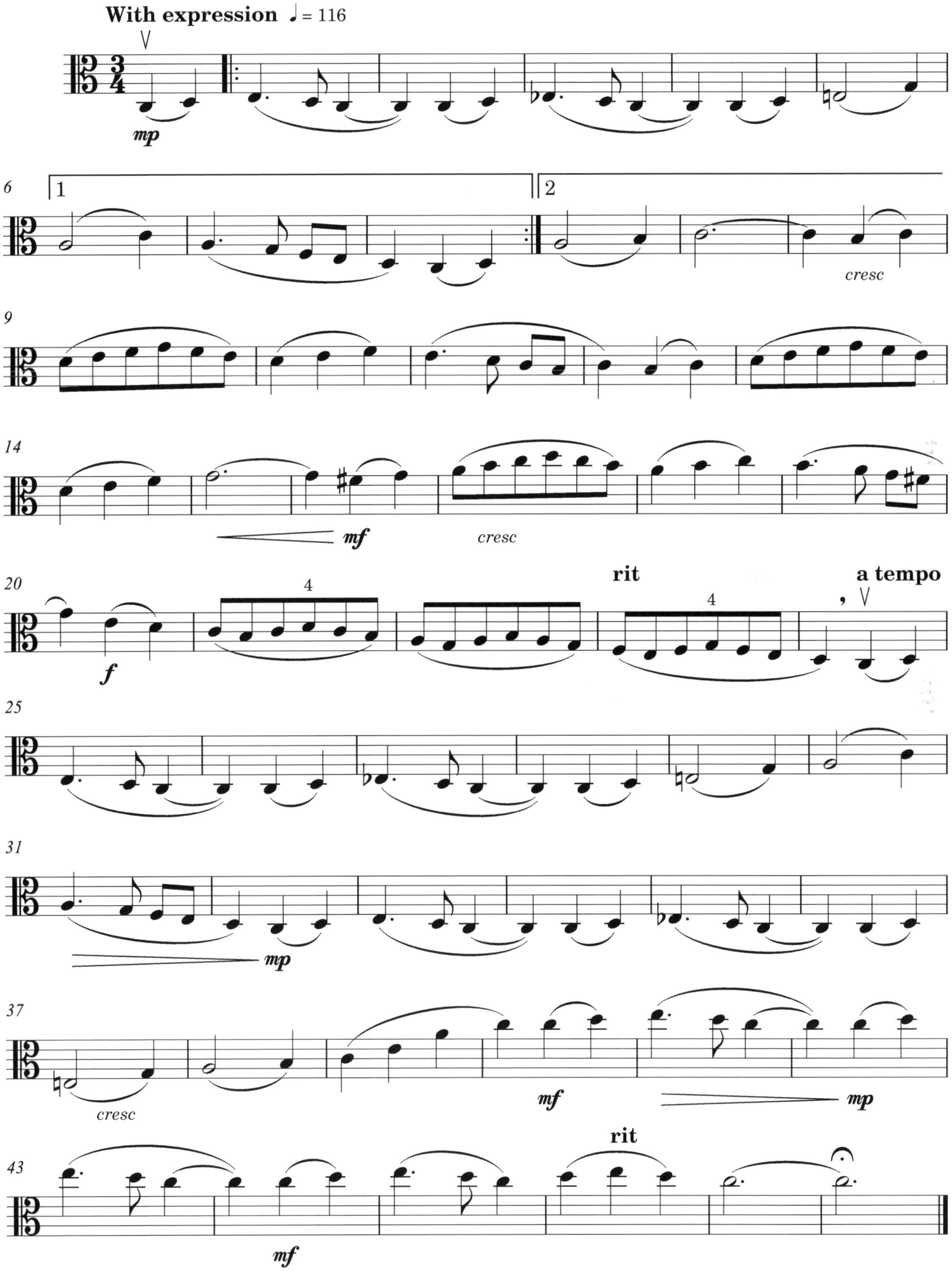

12. **Sweet dreams** (24) (25)

Optional intro: count 2 bars

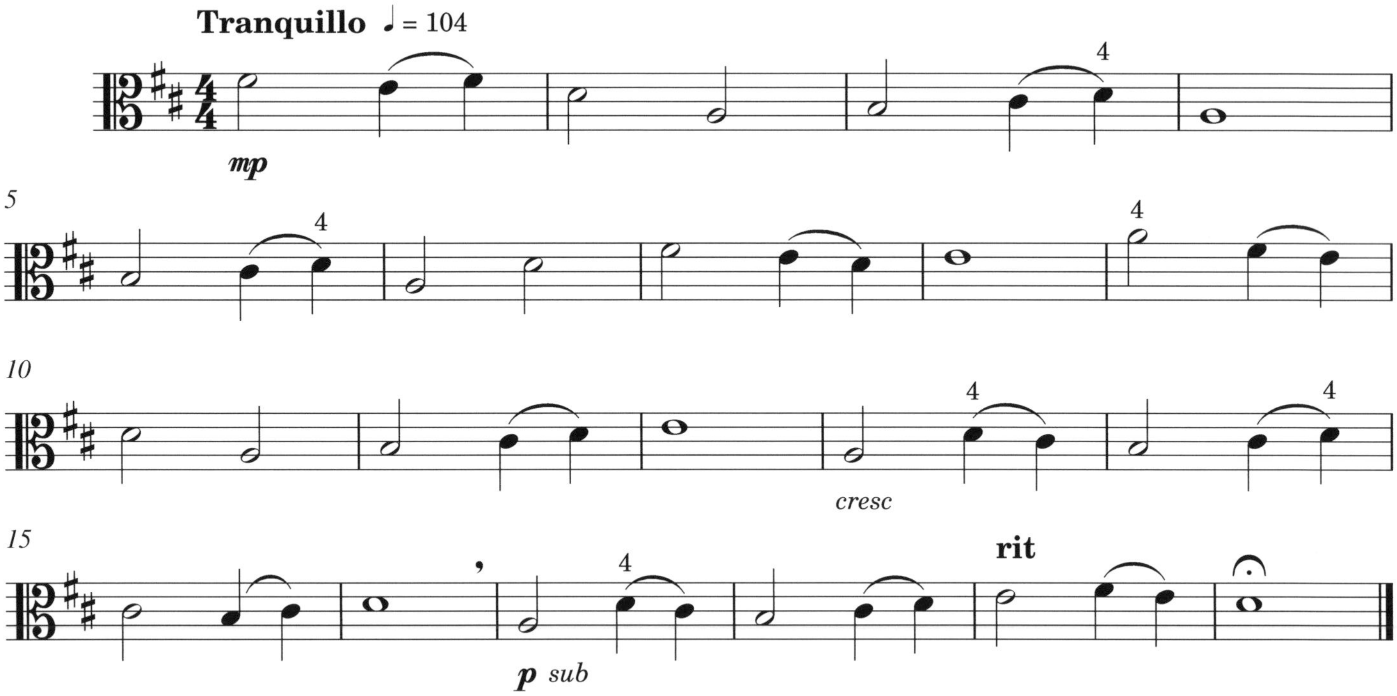

13. **Wondering** (26) (27)

Optional intro: count 2 bars

14. Hustle, bustle

28 29

Optional intro: count 4 bars

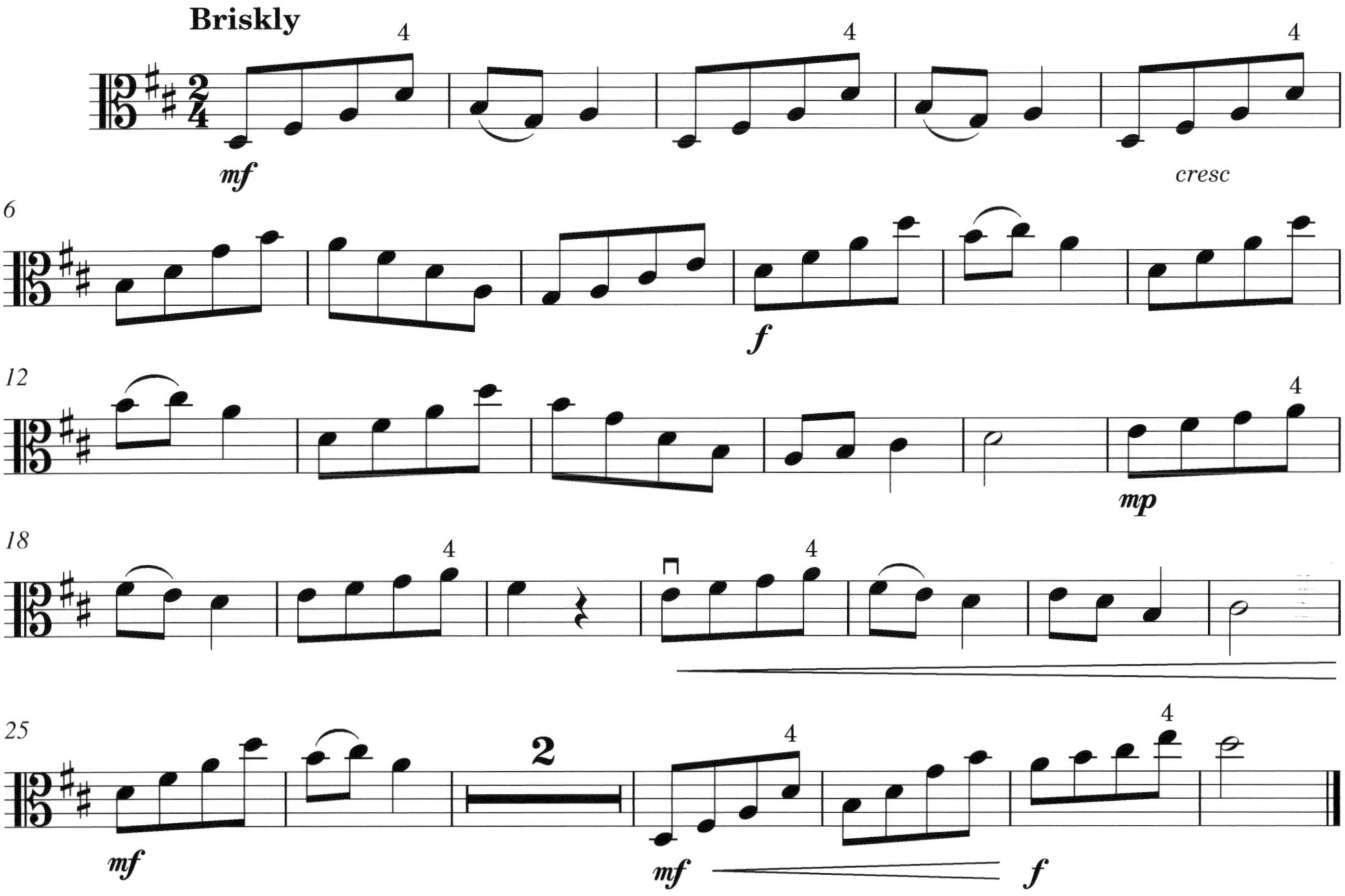

15. Something or other! (for Anna)

30 31

Optional intro: count 2 bars

16. Once upon a time

(32) (33)

17. Fast forward

(34) (35)

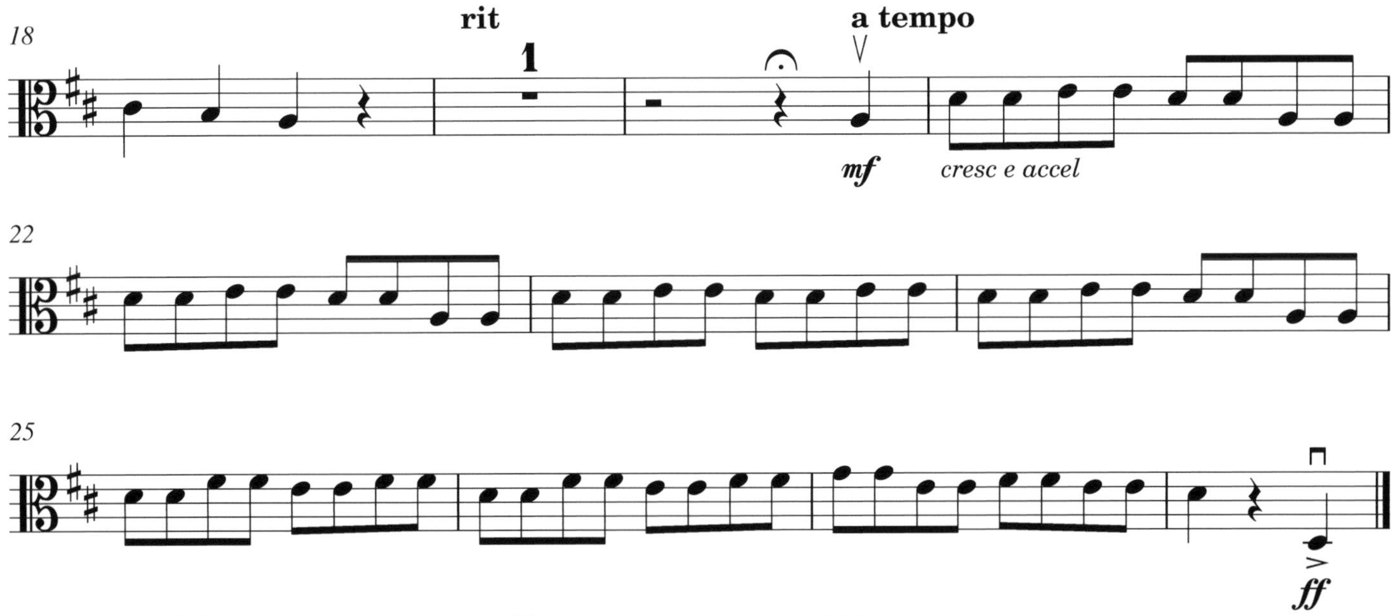

18. What's the time?

36 37

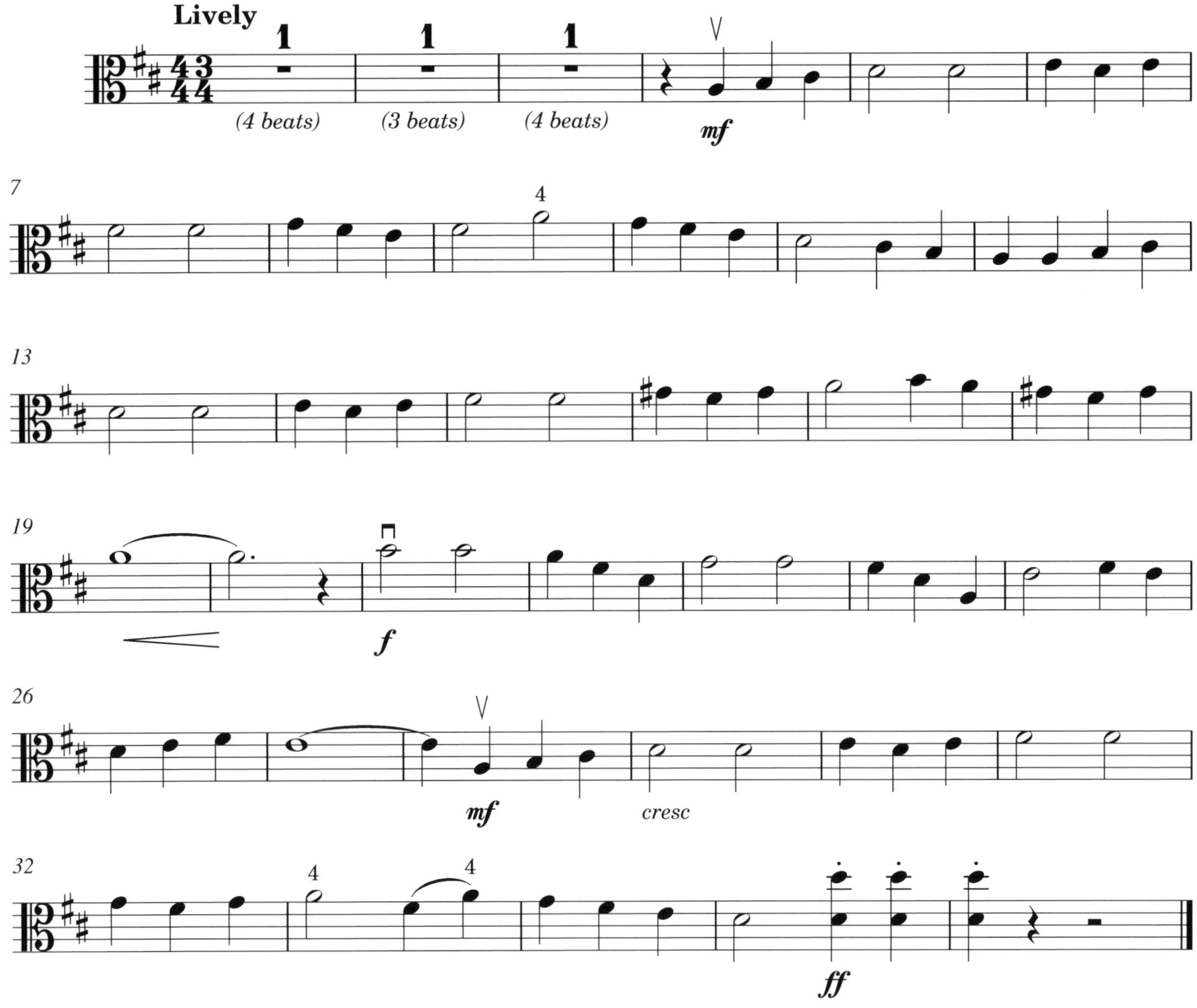

19. **Hornpipe**

(38) (39)

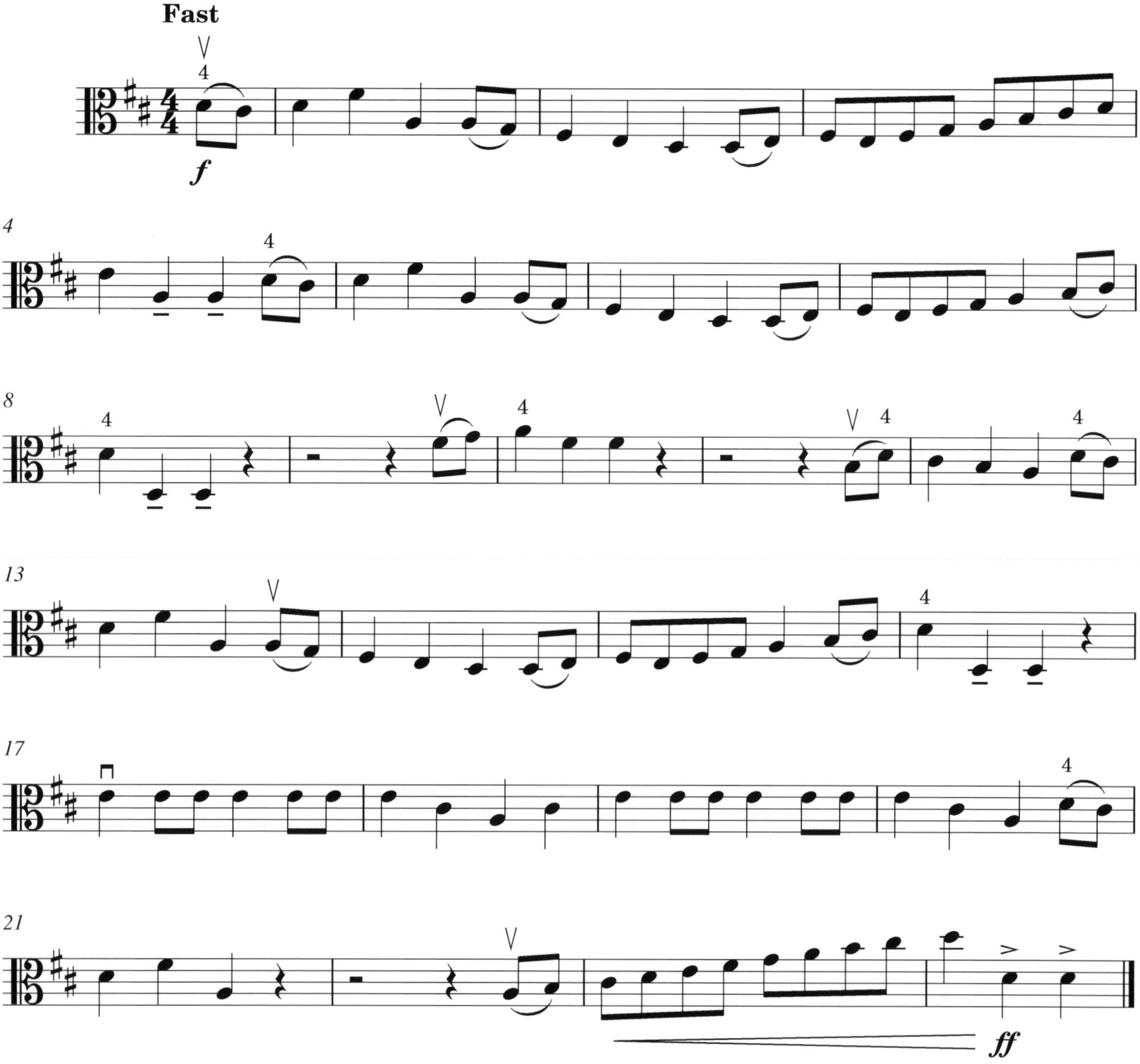

20. **The ceilidh** *(a gathering for traditional music making and dancing in Scotland or Ireland)*

(40) (41)

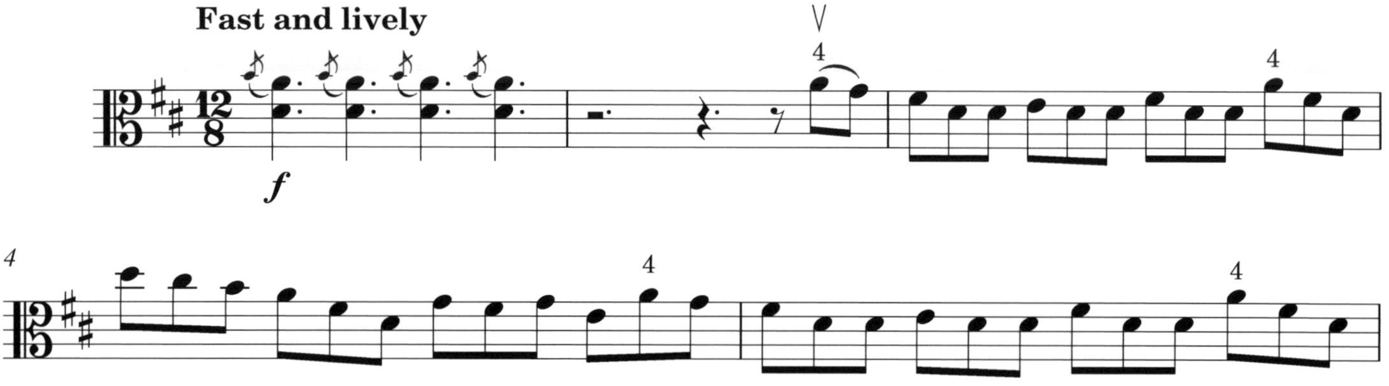

21. Snake charmer

42 43

Optional intro: count 2 bars

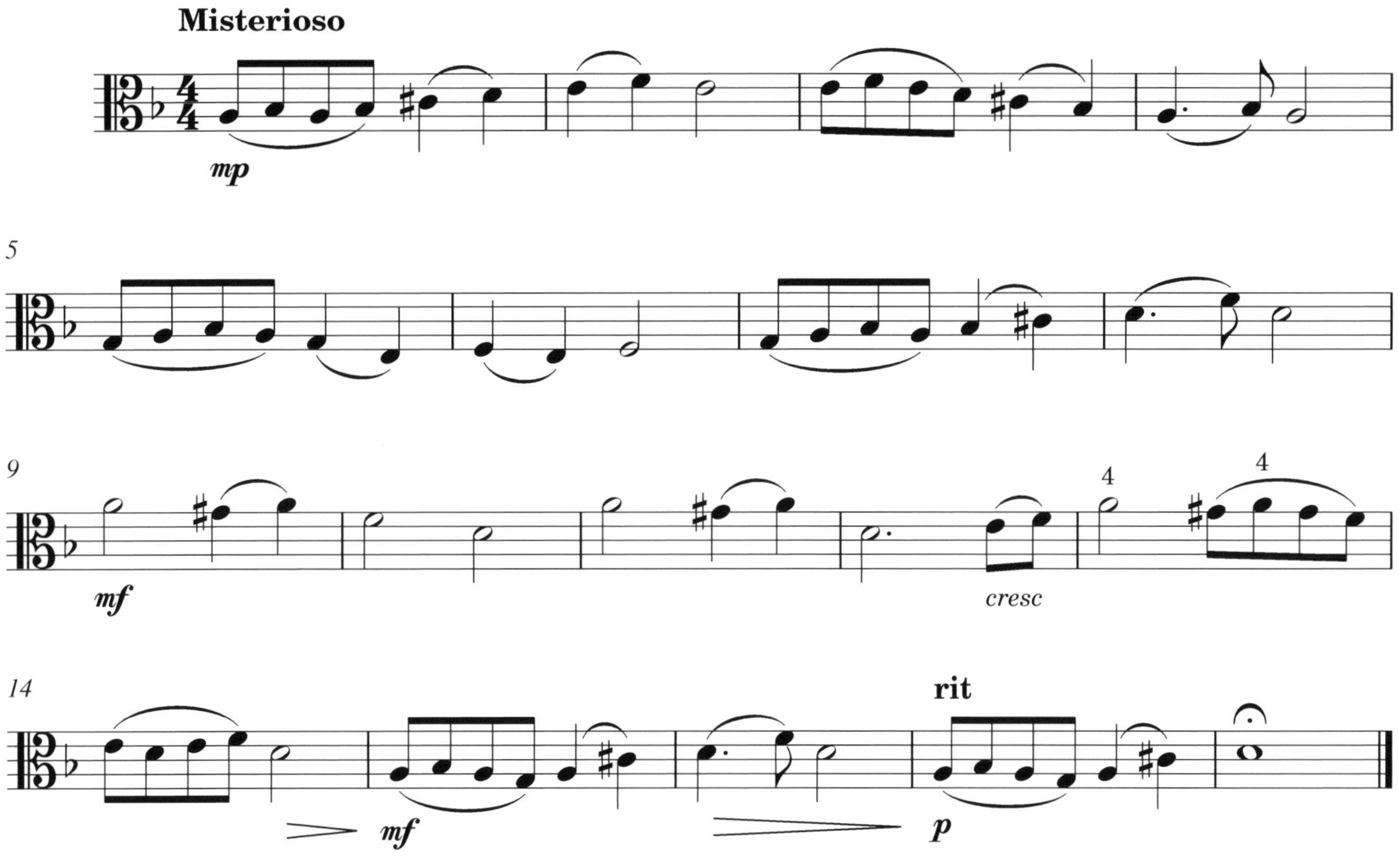

ALSO AVAILABLE FROM BOOSEY & HAWKES

SIMPLY 4 STRINGS

Katherine & Hugh Colledge

A Caribbean Suite
ISMN 979-0-060-12291-0

A Celtic Suite
ISMN 979-0-060-12465-5

A French Suite
ISMN 979-0-060-12098-5

A Handel Suite
ISMN 979-0-060-11957-6

A Yuletide Suite
ISMN 979-0-060-11955-2

An American Suite
ISMN 979-0-060-12099-2

Well-known melodies from around the world arranged for elementary string ensemble.
All the parts are easy yet rewarding, ensuring everyone can join in.
Complete with piano accompaniment, as well as optional parts for viola and double bass.
Ideal for group teaching and concerts.

4 STRINGS

THE COMPLETE CONTEMPORARY REPERTOIRE SERIES FOR STRING QUARTET

Edited by Liz Partridge

Featuring music by
Sally Beamish • Diana Burrell • Katherine & Hugh Colledge • Rupert Gillett
Thomas Hewitt Jones • Rachel Jennings • Richard Kershaw • James MacMillan
Peter McGowan • John Glenesk Mortimer • Christopher Norton • Astor Piazzolla
Rona Porter • Max Richter • Philip Sawyers • Ed Scolding • Rachel Stott

DISCOVER | BOOK 1
for new and developing ensembles

Score & CD with set of parts
ISMN 979-0-060-13375-6
ISBN 978-1-78454-321-1

Score & CD
ISMN 979-0-060-13096-0
ISBN 978-1-78454-162-0

Set of parts
ISMN 979-0-060-13339-8
ISBN 978-1-78454-290-0

EXPLORE | BOOK 2
for flourishing ensembles

Score & CD with set of parts
ISMN 979-0-060-13376-3
ISBN 978-1-78454-322-8

Score & CD
ISMN 979-0-060-13097-7
ISBN 978-1-78454-163-7

Set of parts
ISMN 979-0-060-13340-4
ISBN 978-1-78454-291-7

PIONEER | BOOK 3
for established ensembles

Score & CD with set of parts
ISMN 979-0-060-13377-0
ISBN 978-1-78454-323-5

Score & CD
ISMN 979-0-060-13098-4
ISBN 978-1-78454-164-4

Set of parts
ISMN 979-0-060-13341-1
ISBN 978-1-78454-292-4

BOOSEY & HAWKES

AD 531